For information address Disney Press, 1200 Grand Central Avenue,
Glendale, California 91201.
Printed in China
First Hardcover Edition, January 2018
3 5 7 9 10 8 6 4
ISBN 978-1-368-02182-1
FAC-023680-19152
For more Disney Press fun, visit www.disneybooks.com
This book was printed on paper created from a sustainable source.
#DisneyBaby

Things That Go

Mickey's **ambulance** races to the rescue.

Goofy's **motorcycle** zooms down the street.

Captain Hook's **boat** floats past a crocodile.

Splish-splash!

Carl and Russell's **hot-air balloon** rises into the sky.

Judy chases the bad guys
in her **police car**.

Whoop-whoop
whoop-whoop!

Choo-choo!

Chugga-chugga!

All aboard!

Dumbo's **train**
chugs along the track.

Chugga-chugga!

Mickey's **plane**
soars through the clouds.

Swoosh!

Minnie's **bus**
bounces down the road.

Beep!
Beep!
Beep!

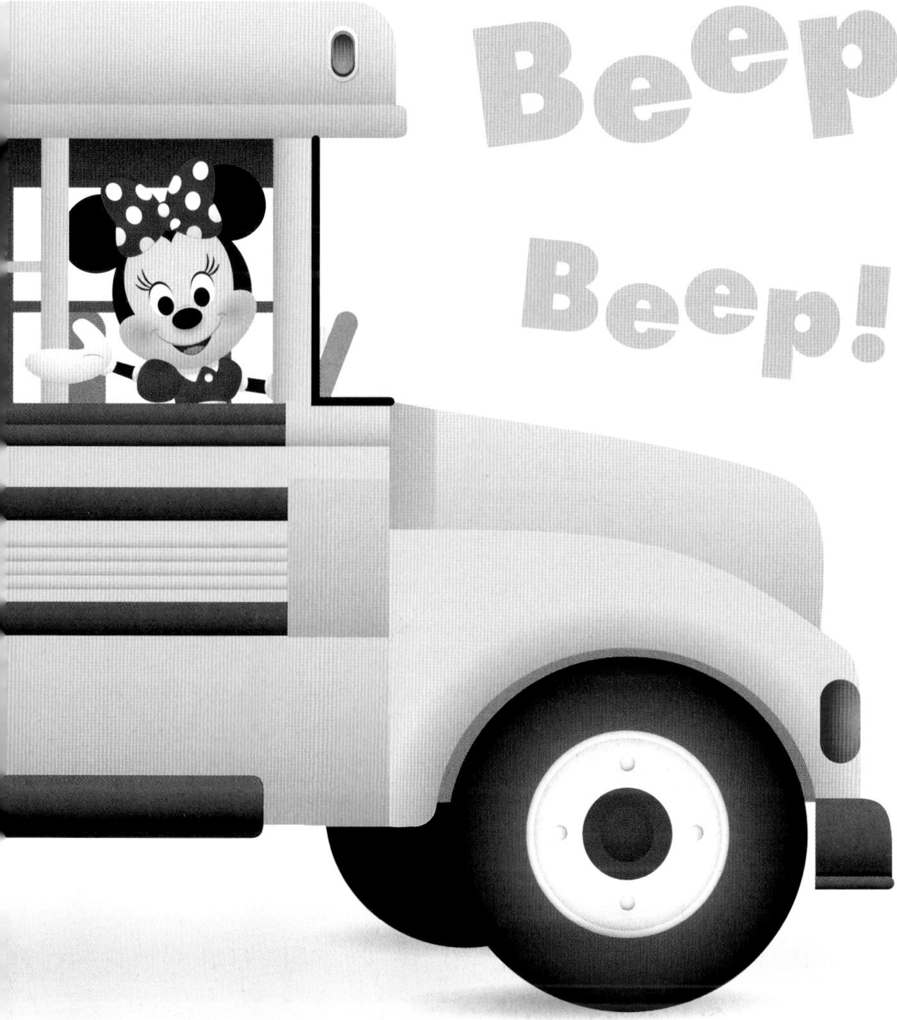

Woody's **fire truck**
is on the move!

Whee-oo whee-oo!

Vanellope's **race car** squeals over the finish line!

Screeeeeeeeech!

Jack-Jack's **stroller** clatters down the street.

Clickety-clack!

Clickety-clack!

Buzz's **spaceship** blasts off!

BooM!